MANUS THE WOLF
TALES FROM THE GLENS

This book belongs to

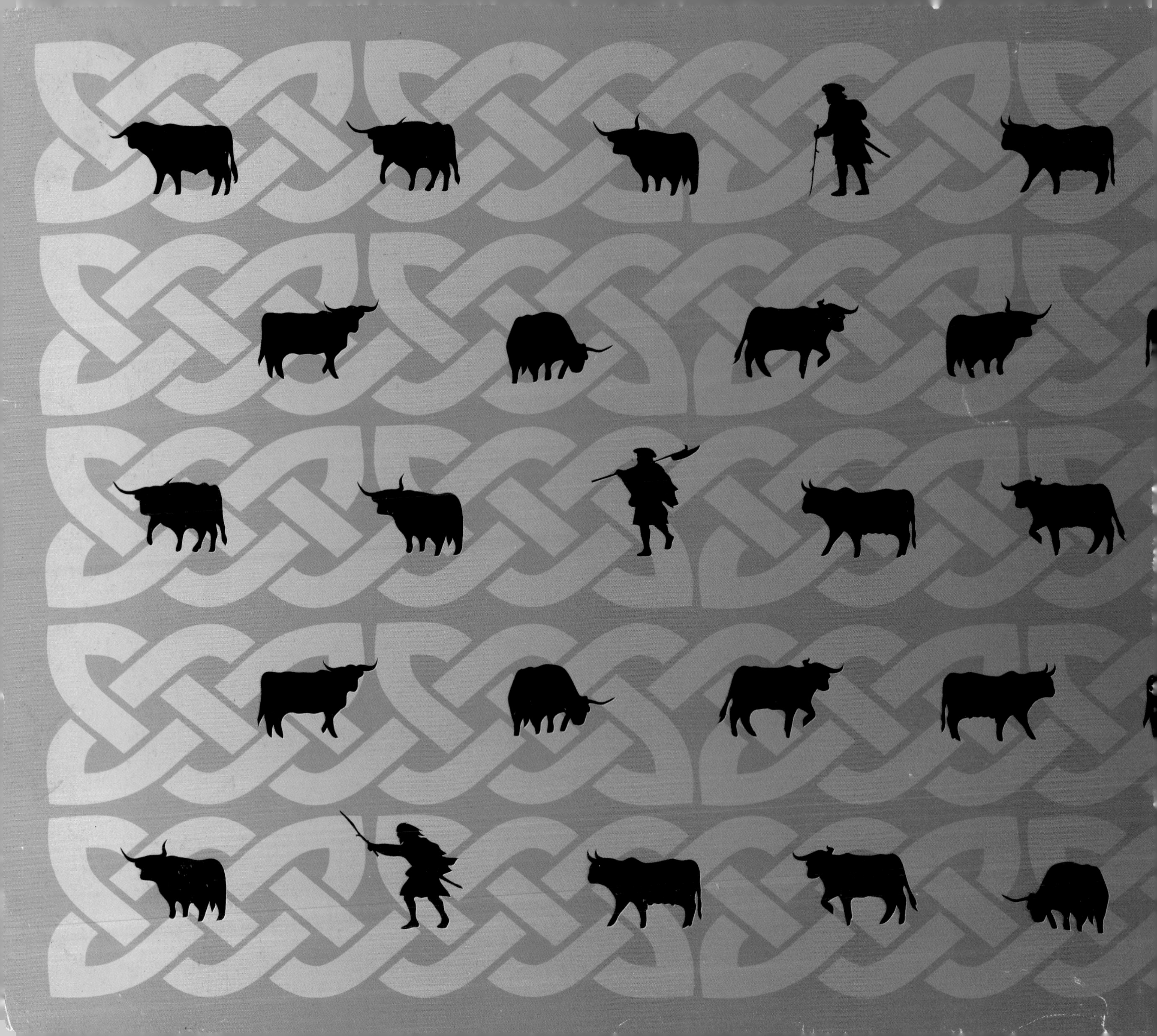

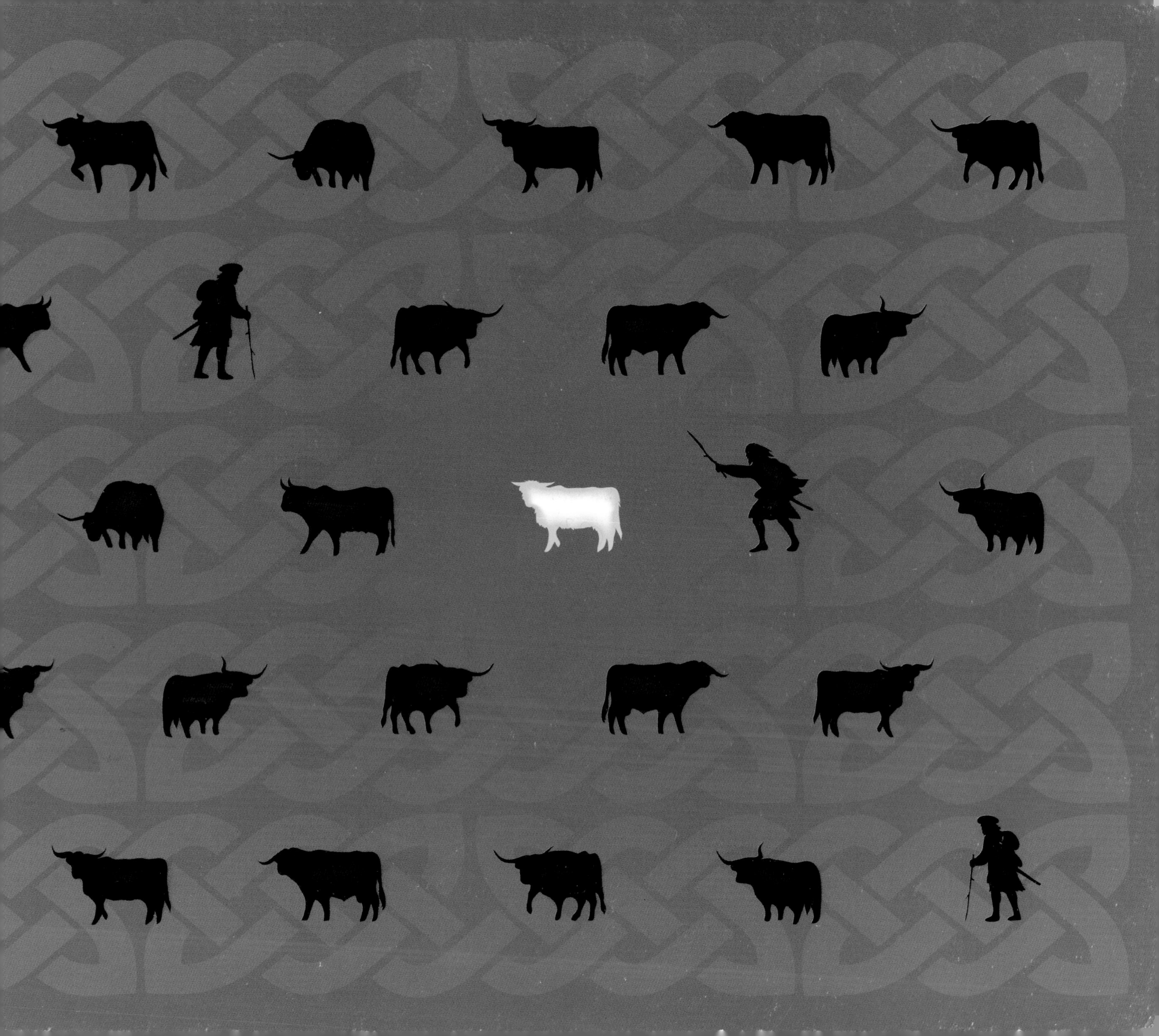

CAPERCAILLIE BOOKS LIMITED

www.capercailliebooks.co.uk

Published by Capercaillie Books Limited,
Registered Office 48 North Castle Street, Edinburgh.

Design by Ian Kirkwood Design.
Printed in Poland.

Set in Catull.

A catalogue record for this book is available from the British Library.

ISBN 0-9542905-9-3

Rob and Bo Ban

by Ian Kirkwood

Capercaillie Books

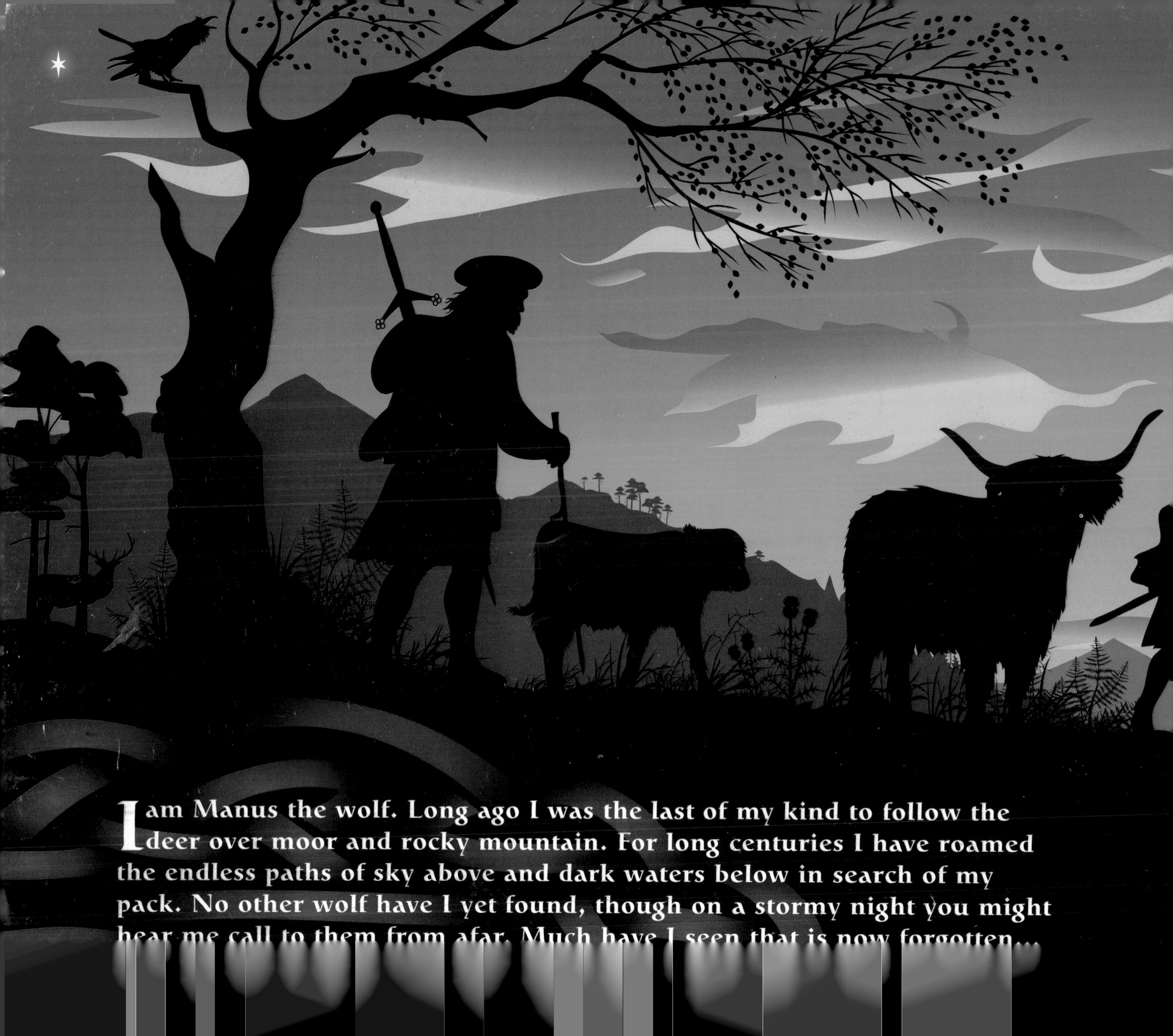

I am Manus the wolf. Long ago I was the last of my kind to follow the deer over moor and rocky mountain. For long centuries I have roamed the endless paths of sky above and dark waters below in search of my pack. No other wolf have I yet found, though on a stormy night you might hear me call to them from afar. Much have I seen that is now forgotten...

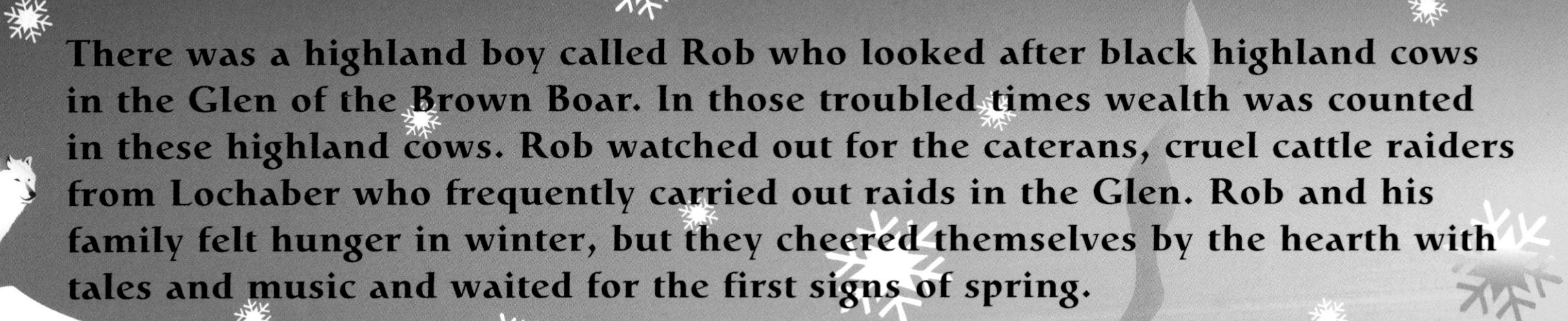

There was a highland boy called Rob who looked after black highland cows in the Glen of the Brown Boar. In those troubled times wealth was counted in these highland cows. Rob watched out for the caterans, cruel cattle raiders from Lochaber who frequently carried out raids in the Glen. Rob and his family felt hunger in winter, but they cheered themselves by the hearth with tales and music and waited for the first signs of spring.

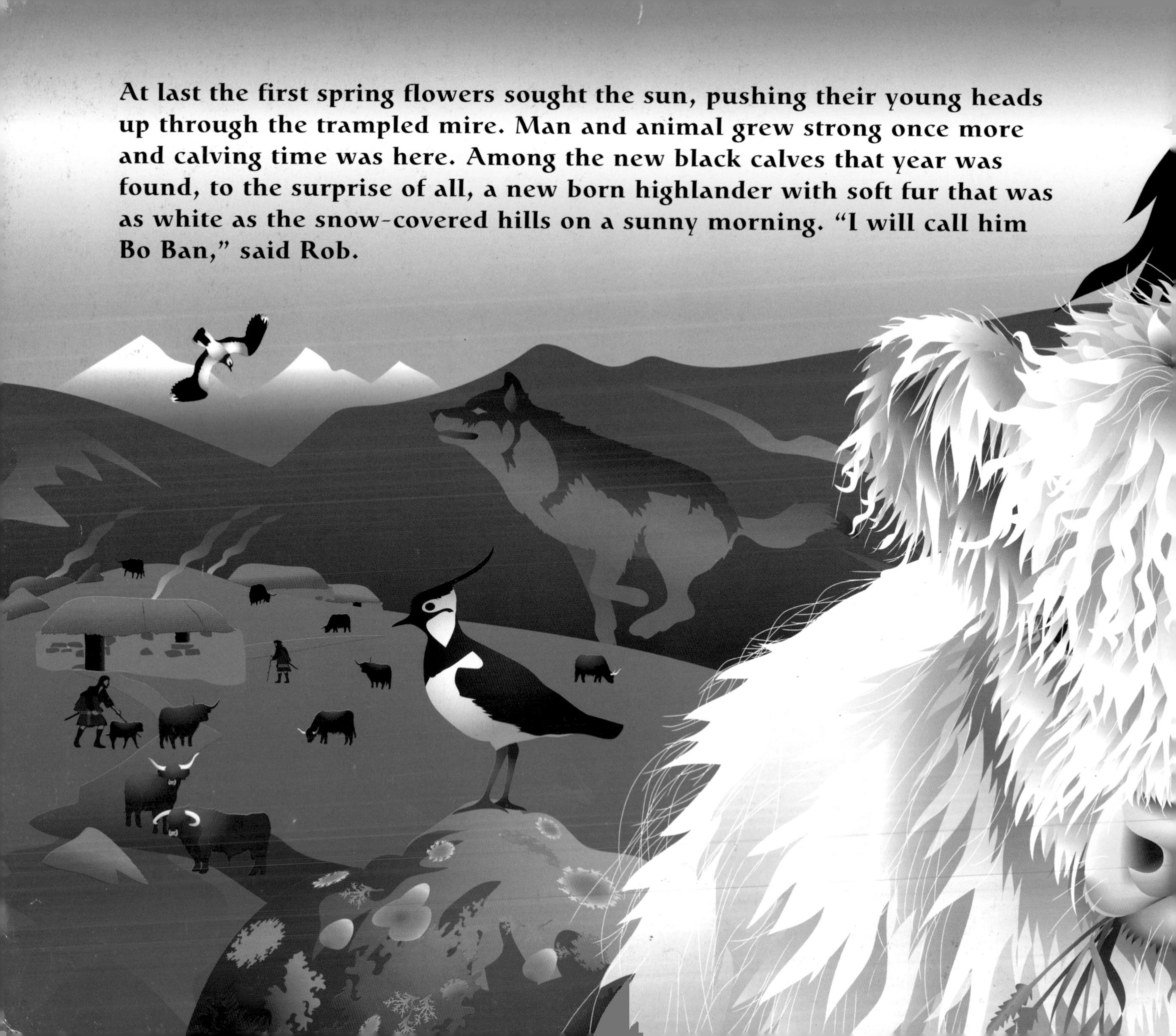

At last the first spring flowers sought the sun, pushing their young heads up through the trampled mire. Man and animal grew strong once more and calving time was here. Among the new black calves that year was found, to the surprise of all, a new born highlander with soft fur that was as white as the snow-covered hills on a sunny morning. "I will call him Bo Ban," said Rob.

Summer arrived and Rob led his herd to the best grazing he could find. He grew fond of the white calf, watching him as he grew up grazing peacefully on the hillside. For his part, Bo Ban felt safe knowing that Rob was never far away. Rob lay down on the heather and stared at a lark singing high in the blue sky. "This is the life!" thought Rob.

One hot day the highland cows stood in the burn to cool their hooves, their tails swishing at flies. As evening approached Rob left them to go further up the burn to guddle a trout. He peered around a large rock. A trout was resting in its shade. Rob lay on the bank and stretched his arm down through the water to tickle the trout's belly. Just as he was about to flick the fish on to the bank he heard shouting below.

Rob ran. He cried out. Armed caterans were driving the highland cows out of the Glen. Rob waved his dirk in the air. “You villains!” shouted Rob. But the raiders only laughed at him. As they disappeared over the hills Bo Ban turned and looked for Rob before being driven on by the raiders. Rob breathed fast. What could he do on his own against so many men? “Poor Bo Ban!” said Rob, “How will I get him back?”

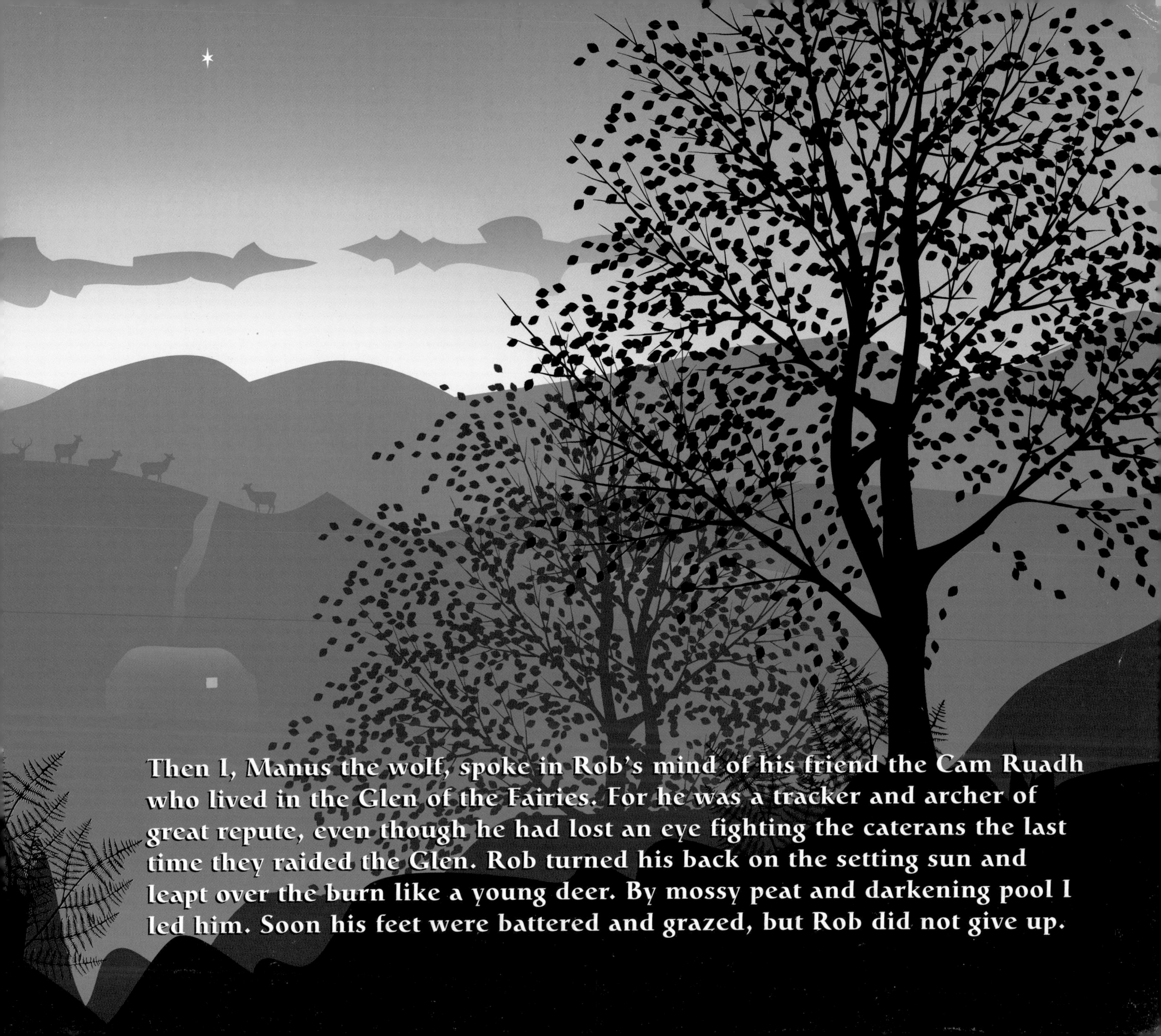

Then I, Manus the wolf, spoke in Rob's mind of his friend the Cam Ruadh who lived in the Glen of the Fairies. For he was a tracker and archer of great repute, even though he had lost an eye fighting the caterans the last time they raided the Glen. Rob turned his back on the setting sun and leapt over the burn like a young deer. By mossy peat and darkening pool I led him. Soon his feet were battered and grazed, but Rob did not give up.

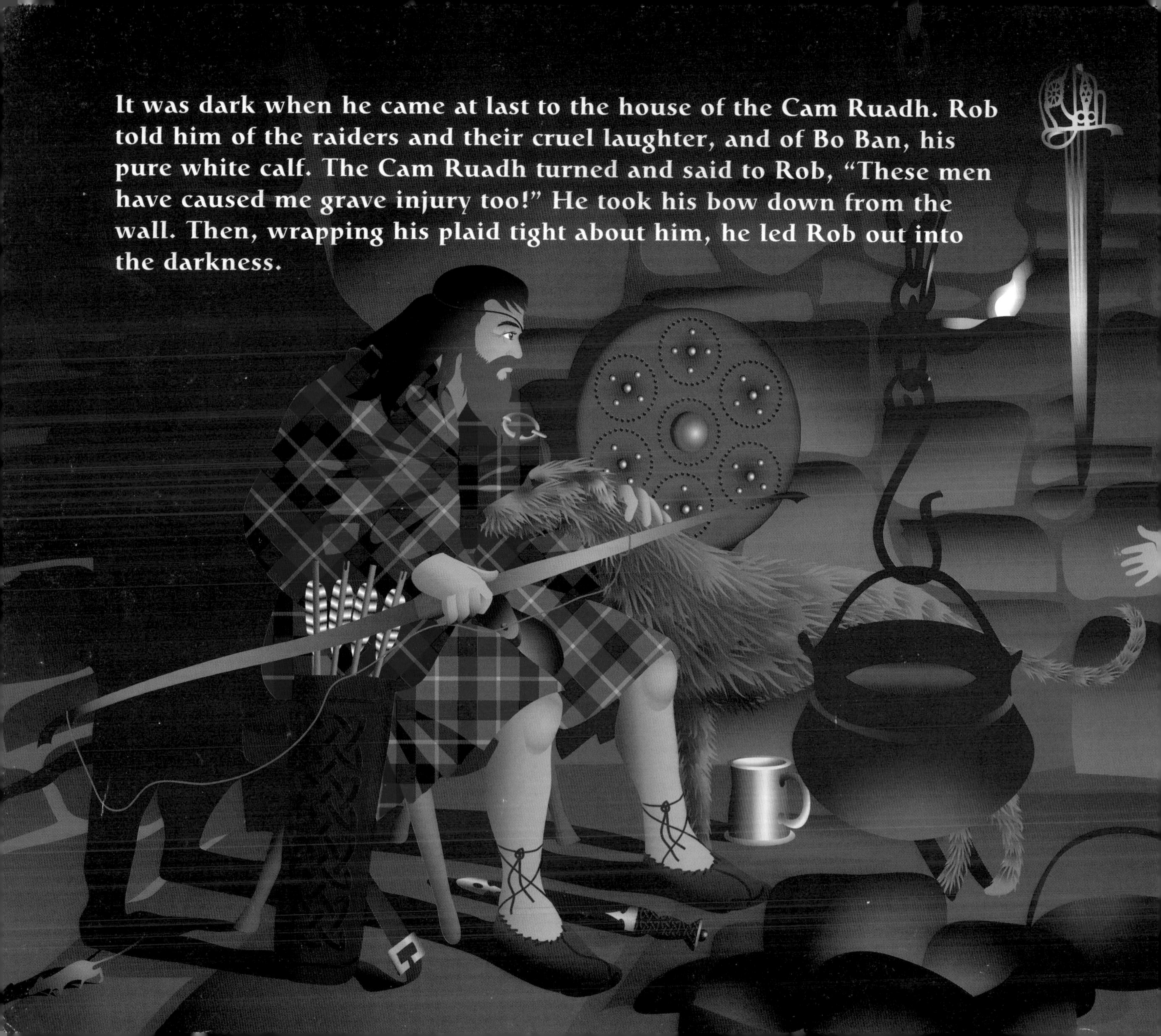

It was dark when he came at last to the house of the Cam Ruadh. Rob told him of the raiders and their cruel laughter, and of Bo Ban, his pure white calf. The Cam Ruadh turned and said to Rob, "These men have caused me grave injury too!" He took his bow down from the wall. Then, wrapping his plaid tight about him, he led Rob out into the darkness.

It was not difficult to follow the tracks, for the caterans had made raids throughout the Glen and the herd was now large. Rob knew he was on course whenever his foot sank into a warm pile of fresh dung. The sky was star-studded when the Cam Ruadh sensed the herd close

Then in the gloom, dimly outlined in the blackness, one thing became visible: the unmistakable form of Bo Ban trying to keep up with the fast moving herd. The Cam Ruadh closed in. When he heard Bo Ban being hit with a stick, he chose a spot a little behind the white calf and sent the arrow speeding into the darkness. A muffled yelp escaped the invisible but unlucky raider whose job it had been to keep the slower animals moving.

As Bo Ban slowed his pace Rob heard a rough voice ordering another of the raiding party to the rear to keep the herd moving. It was not long before a second arrow was loosed into the dark. Tempers ran high as the third man made his way back to the white calf. But once it was realised he too was gone, first doubt, then fear gripped the caterans. One more fell before those remaining fled for their lives.

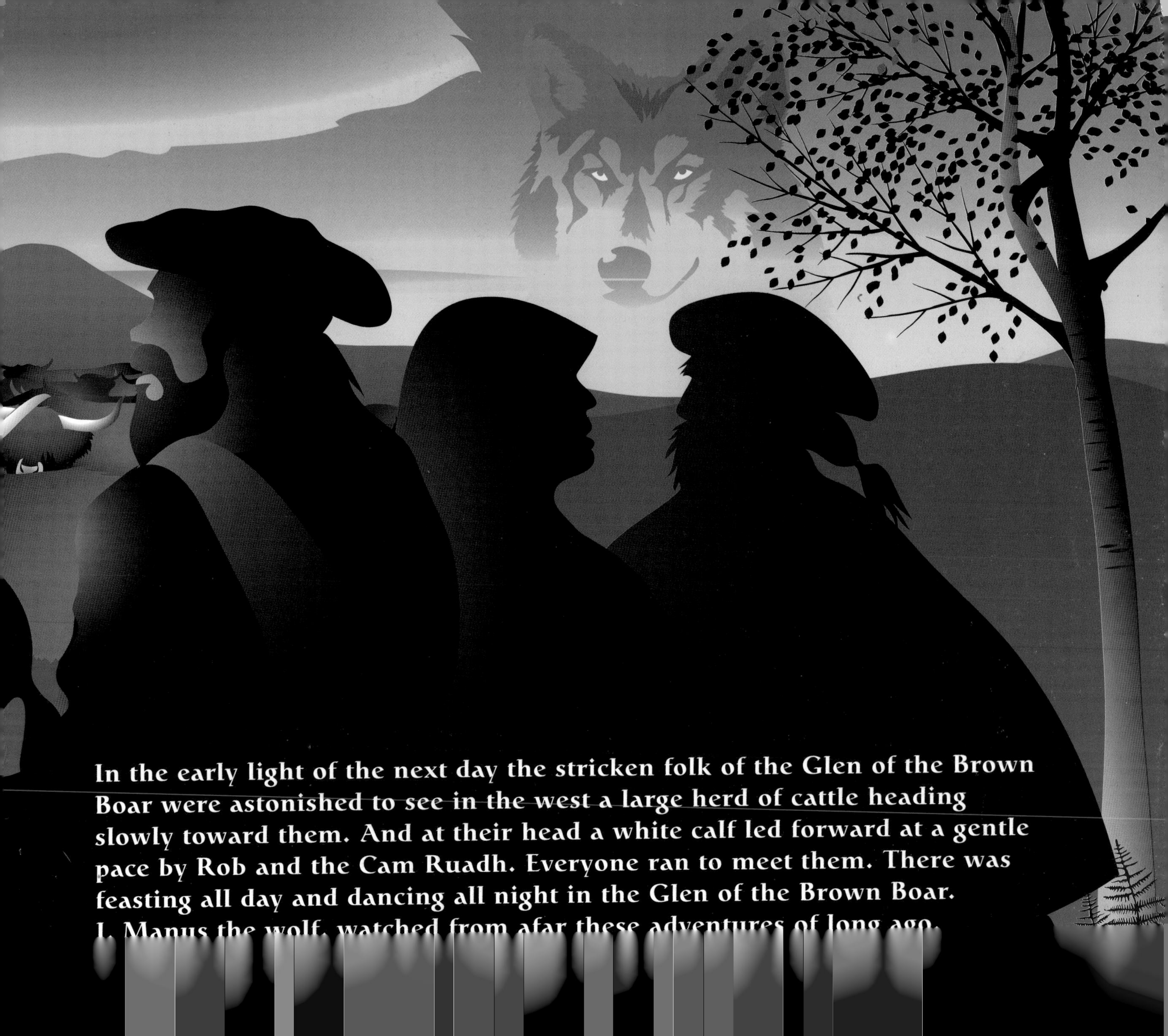

In the early light of the next day the stricken folk of the Glen of the Brown Boar were astonished to see in the west a large herd of cattle heading slowly toward them. And at their head a white calf led forward at a gentle pace by Rob and the Cam Ruadh. Everyone ran to meet them. There was feasting all day and dancing all night in the Glen of the Brown Boar.
I, Manus the wolf, watched from afar these adventures of long ago.

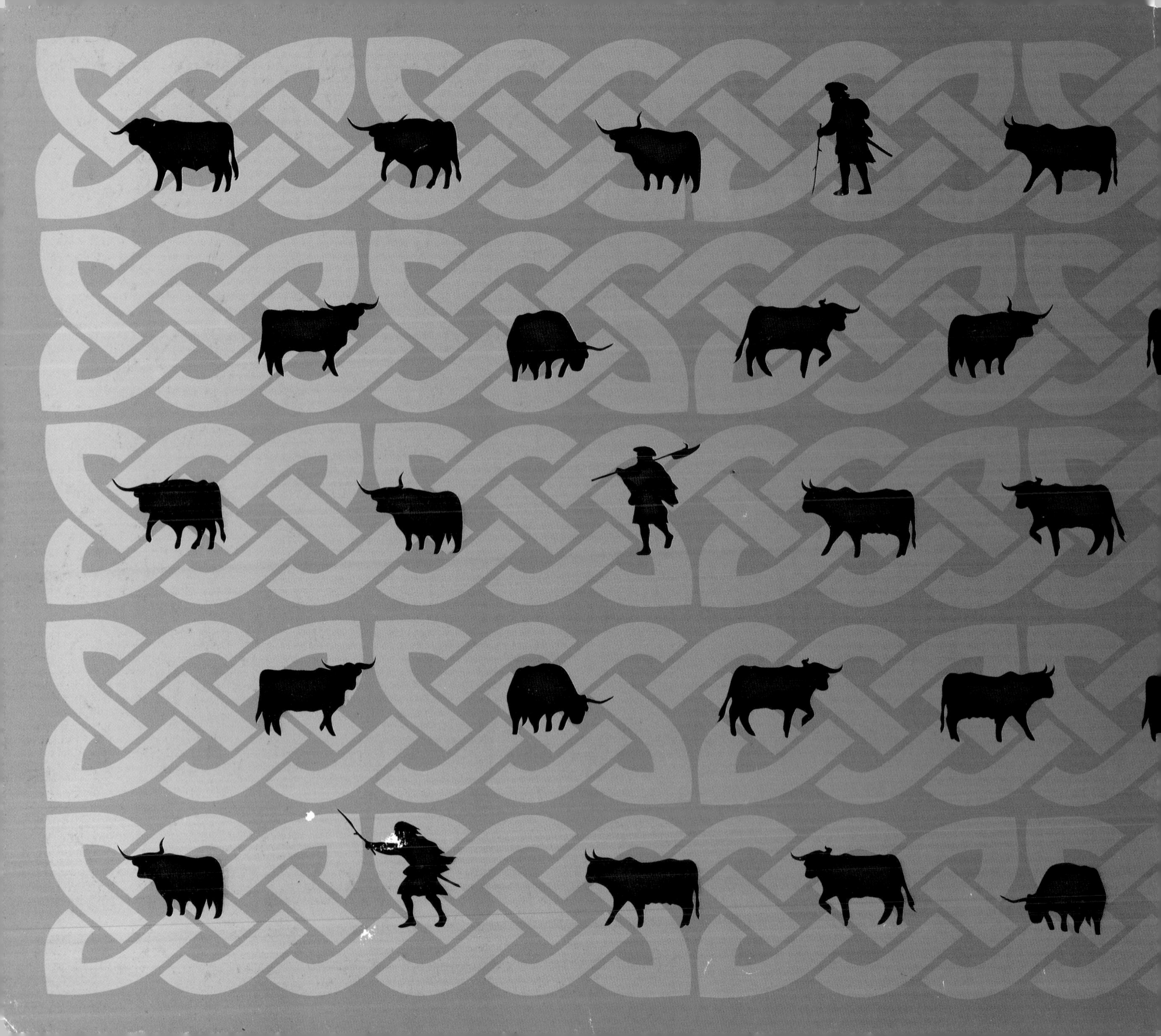

Historical Note

In the 1640s John Grant, known in Gaelic as the Cam Ruadh (the One-eyed Red Head) lived in Glen Taitneach above Glen Shee. His formidable archery skills were called upon to help the people of Strathardle (once known as the Glen of the Brindled Boar) in the face of increasingly disastrous raids by the men of Lochaber. A white cow was indeed the means by which he outwitted the raiders. It is said the stones of the Allt-Chroskie burn, where the last of the band was overtaken, were stained red with blood. The author acknowledges the work of Charles Fergusson who set down this tale in the 1890s in a paper presented to The Gaelic Society of Inverness.

Capercaillie Books